The well known parable of the Prodigal Son
is retold simply in this delightfully illustrated
version and will appeal to all young listeners
and early readers.

The story is based on the gospel of St Luke,
chapter 15, verses 11-32.

British Library Cataloguing in Publication Data
Hately, David
    The prodigal son.
    1. Bible. N.T. Parables: Prodigal son
    I. Title   II. Drabble, Helen   III. Series
    226'.
    ISBN 0-7214-9589-3

First Edition
Published by Ladybird Books Ltd Loughborough Leicestershire UK
Ladybird Books Inc Auburn Maine 04210 USA

Printed in England

The Prodigal Son

written by DAVID HATELY
illustrated by HELEN DRABBLE

Ladybird Books

A rich man had two sons. He didn't have a favourite. He loved each as much as the other.

The elder son wanted to stay at home and help his father to look after their lands.

The younger son wanted to leave home. He thought he would go away and enjoy himself.

The loving father told his sons that one day he would give them everything he owned.

Each of them would get an equal share.

But the younger son said, "I want my share now!"

The younger son took his share of the money and he left home to have a good time.

His father was sad to see him go. But he loved his son, and did not make him stay at home.

The young man travelled through many lands. He never thought about his home. He was too busy spending his money on things for himself.

Soon, he had wasted
everything and he had
no money left.

Then there was a terrible famine in the land where the young man was living.

Even for people who had money, it was hard to buy food.

But the young man had nothing, and he grew very hungry.

He tried to get a job, but jobs were hard to find.

In the end, he went to a farmer and asked if he could look after the pigs.

The young man was paid no wages. All he got was some of the food the pigs ate.

At night, instead of sleeping, he began to think about his home. He had been warm and comfortable and well fed there.

When he thought about his loving father, he began to cry. But he was too ashamed to go home.

One day, tired and hungry and lonely, he said to himself, "My father's servants have as much as they want to eat. They're clean and well dressed. They have comfortable beds to sleep in.

"I will leave this terrible place and go to my father and say I am sorry for turning my back on him. I don't deserve to be his son, but perhaps he'll let me be one of his servants."

The young man made his way home.

When his father saw him he ran out to meet him.
His heart was bursting with joy as he put his
arms round his son and kissed him.
"Welcome home, son,"
he said.

"I don't deserve to be your son any more,"
the boy answered. "Just treat me as
one of your servants."

But the loving father said to his servants,
"Quick! Bring my son the best clothes you can
find! Then get ready for a great party! We must
all celebrate! I thought my son was dead
but he has come back to me after all!"

The elder son was out in the fields. When he got home, he heard the music and dancing and soon found out why the special party was being held.

He was jealous of all the fuss they were making over his good-for-nothing brother.

"All my life," he said to his father, "I have worked hard for you and I have never disobeyed you. But you have never bothered to throw a big party for me and my friends."

His father smiled at his elder son, "You are with me all the time, and I love you," he said. "Everything I have is yours already. Don't be jealous because I love your brother, too.

"Remember! It is your *brother* who has come back! So, if you love me, laugh and be glad like me."

This story about the father and his two sons was first told by Jesus.

He is teaching us that God is a generous father.

He is teaching us to love and forgive one another and not be jealous, like the elder son.

And he is teaching us that, because we are his children, God always loves us, no matter what we do or how much we hurt him. All we have to do is to tell him that we are sorry for turning our back on him. If we really mean it, he will say, "Welcome home!"